V & A CATS

BIRTHDAY
B O O K

THE VICTORIA AND ALBERT MUSEUM

CATS

BIRTHDAY BOOK

THE VICTORIA AND ALBERT MUSEUM

C A T S

BIRTHDAY BOOK

EBURY PRESS STATIONERY

FIRST PUBLISHED IN 1992 BY EBURY PRESS STATIONERY
AN IMPRINT OF THE RANDOM CENTURY GROUP
RANDOM CENTURY HOUSE,
20 VAUXHALL BRIDGE ROAD,
LONDON SW1V 2SA
COPYRIGHT © RANDOM CENTURY GROUP 1992
ILLUSTRATIONS © BOARD OF TRUSTEES,
VICTORIA AND ALBERT MUSEUM

SET IN BEMBO BY 🐦 TEK ART LTD,
ADDISCOMBE, CROYDON, SURREY

PRINTED IN ITALY

DESIGNED BY PETER BENNETT

ISBN 0   09175   144   6

WINNING POST

THE FINISH.

JANUARY

1

2

3

4

5

6

7

JANUARY

8 Betty Ferguson

9 Ian Ferguson

10

11

12

13

14

JANUARY

15

16 Paul Jr III

17

18

19

20

21

JANUARY

22

23

24

25

26

27

28

29 *Dennis*

30

31

1

2

3

4

FEBRUARY

5

6

7

8

9

10

11

FEBRUARY

12

13

14

15

16

17

18

FEBRUARY

19

20

21

22

23

24

25

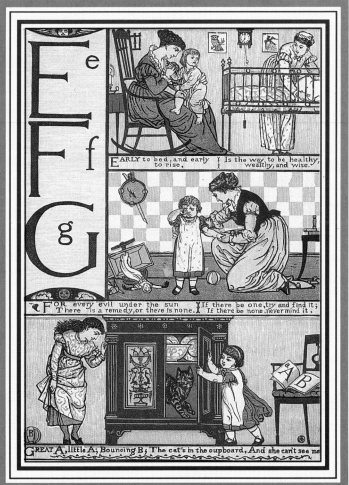

E e
F f
G g

EARLY to bed, and early to rise, Is the way to be healthy, wealthy, and wise.

FOR every evil under the sun There is a remedy, or there is none. If there be one, try and find it; If there be none, never mind it.

GREAT A, little A; Bouncing B; The cat's in the cupboard, And she can't see me.

FEBRUARY – MARCH

26

27

28

29

1

2

3

MARCH

4

5

6 Sarah Jean

7 Phyllis Hughes
Barbie

8 Mom F.

9

10

MARCH

11 Chris Plamondon

12

13

14

15 Patty

16

17

MARCH

18

19 Alison Ferguson

20

21 Tony

22

23

24

cap

pap

lap

lap nap

MARCH

25

26

27

28

29

30

31

APRIL

1

2

3

4 *Penny*

5

6

7

APRIL

8

9

10

11

12

13

14

APRIL

15

16

17

18

19

20

21

APRIL

22

23

24

25

26

27

28

APRIL – MAY

29

30

1

2

3

4

5

MAY

6

7

8

9

10

11

12

MAY

13

14

15

16

17

18

19

MAY

20 Mine F.

21

22

23

24

25

26 Paige

MAY – JUNE

27

28

29

30

31

1

2

WISHING YOU A BRIGHT AND JOYOUS CHRISTMAS.

JUNE

3

4

5

6

7

8

9

JUNE

10

11

12

13

14

15

16

JUNE

17

18

19

20 Rachel Ellen Clark

21

22

23

JUNE

24

25 Me

26 Kiaya Rene

27 Dick J.

28

29

30

JULY

1

2

3

4

5 *Janet Ferguson*

6

7

JULY

8

9

10

11

12

13 Keenan Klaus
    Mary

14

JULY

15

16

17

18

19 ~~Sandi~~

20 Sandip

21 Anne Ferguson

JULY

22

23

24

25

26

27

28

29 *Travis*
Gabrielle

30

31

1

2

3

4

AUGUST

5 Mom B.

6

7

8

9

10

11

AUGUST

12

13

14

15

16

17

18

AUGUST

19

20

21

22

23

24

25

AUGUST – SEPTEMBER

26

27

28

29

30

31

1

SEPTEMBER

2

3

4

5

6

7

8

SEPTEMBER

9

10

11

12 ~~Processes~~

13

14

15

SEPTEMBER

16 *Ashley*

17

18

19

20

21

22

Louis Wain.

SEPTEMBER

23

24 Mikaela Ellen Klaus
Hanson

25

26

27

28

29

30

1

2

3

4

5 Sue Leohr Daniels

6

OCTOBER

7 *Caitlin Ferguson*

8

9

10

11

12

13

WITH THE COMPLIMENTS OF THE SEASON.

OCTOBER

14

15

16

17

18 *Pam*
Cheryl

19

20

OCTOBER

21 Leah Elizabeth Clark

22

23

24

25

26

27

28

29 Laurie Kay Samuels
Ballweber

30

31

1

2

3

NOVEMBER

4

5

6

7

8

9

10 *Jr Leohn*

NOVEMBER

11 John Ferguson

12 Phillip Michael

13 Paul Jr.

14

15

16

17

NOVEMBER

18

19

20

21

22

23

24

NOVEMBER – DECEMBER

25

26

27

28

29

30   David Ferguson

1   Paul, Sr.

E EAT IT

DECEMBER

2

3

4 Harry Breem

5

6

7

8

DECEMBER

9

10

11

12

13

14

15

DECEMBER

16

17

18

19

20

21

22

DECEMBER

23

24

25

26

27

28

29

DECEMBER

30

31

PICTURE CREDITS IN
CHRONOLOGICAL ORDER

Page from *The Kitten's Garden of Verses*, Oliver Herford, 1911. Renier Collection, BGM.

White Cat; Ethel Mars, *c*.1900. Colour print from woodblock.

Christmas card of a cat's bicycle race; late 19th century. Colour lithograph.

Seated Cat; Gwen John, *c*.1920. Watercolour.

Three Black Cats; Louis Wain; design for children's writing paper, *c*.1920. Indian ink, water and bodycolour.

'Poor Seraphim'; illustration by Topham from *The Chummy Book* 15th year. Renier Collection, BGM.

'She made them some broth'; illustration by Cecil Aldin and John Hassall from *Two Well-Worn Shoe Stories*, 1899. BGM.

Portrait of a Child; James Northcote, 1795. Oil on canvas.

Advertisement for Edward's Dessicated Soup; E.E. Shepheard, *c*.1900. Chromolithograph.

Page from *The Rubaiyat of a Persian Kitten*; Oliver Herford, 1904. Renier Collection, BGM.

Illustration from *Baby's Own Alphabet* by Professor Meiklejohn and Walter Crane, 1860s.

'Asking two yokels the way', Puss in Boots by Gordon Robinson. Original watercolour. Renier Collection, BGM.

Page from *A Peep into Catland* by Constance Howell, 1890. Renier Collection, BGM.

'Puss in Corner' from *Christmas Roses* by Lizzie Lawson and Robert Mack, 1886.

Illustration from *The Golden Primer*; Walter Crane, 1860s.

'Hey Diddle Diddle' from *The Second Collection of Pictures and Songs*, by R. Caldecott. London 1882.

Page from *The Kitten's Garden of Verses*; Oliver Herford, 1911. Renier Collection, BGM.

Advertisement for a cabaret; T. Steinlen, 1896. Colour lithograph.

'Wedding', Puss in Boots, by Gordon Robinson. Original watercolour. Renier Collection, BGM.

Page from *Three Kittens in a Boat*, by Geraldine Robinson, 1920. Renier Collection, BGM.

Illustration from *Through the Meadows* by Fred Weatherly; illustrations by M. Edwards, London 1880s.

'Approaching the Castle Gates', Puss in Boots, by Gordon Robinson. Original watercolour. Renier Collection, BGM.

Two cats; T. Steinlen, 1894. Colour lithograph.

Page from *The Rubaiyat of a Persian Kitten*; Oliver Herford, 1904. Renier Collection, BGM.

Christmas card; late 19th century. Colour lithograph.

'The Introduction'; illustration by Alan Wright for Blackie's Children's Annual 22nd year. Renier Collection, BGM.

Page from *The Kitten's*

Garden of Verses; Oliver Herford, 1911. Renier Collection, BGM.

'Walking towards a Cliff', Puss in Boots by Gordon Robinson. Original watercolour.

Christmas card; 1865–90. Colour lithograph.

Cat. Chinese, *c*. 1850. Watercolour.

Painting from an album of Chinese watercolours; 19th century.

Page from *The Rubaiyat of a Persian Kitten*; Oliver Herford, 1904. Renier Collection, BGM.

Black Cat; Elizabeth Blackadder, 1985. Lithograph. Courtesy of the artist.

The Hhareem; J.F. Lewis (1805–1876). Watercolour.

Advertisement for *Tit-Bits* magazine; C. Amyot, *c*.1900. Colour lithograph.

Interior of a School, Cairo; J.F. Lewis, 1858. Watercolour.

Two Cats; T. Steinlen, 1914. Ink drawing.

Christmas card; *c*.1900. Colour lithograph.

Smiling cat; *c*.1930. Colour print. Renier Collection, BGM.

Page from *The Kitten's Garden of Verses*; Oliver Herford, 1911. Renier Collection, BGM.

In Sunny Spain; Louis Wain, *c*.1910–20. Indian ink, water and bodycolour.

Toy cat, black fur fabric. German *c*.1935.

Cat from a scrapbook.

Christmas card; *c*.1900. Colour lithograph.

Hallo There! We won't go home till morning; Louis Wain, *c*.1900–10. Indian ink, water and bodycolour.

Page from *The Kitten's Garden of Verses*; Oliver Herford, 1911. Renier Collection, BGM.

The Barrier; Sir Edwin Landseer, 1832. Oil on canvas.

Hey Diddle Diddle; Edith Cubitt, *c*.1910. Renier Collection, BGM.

Russian book illustration; Marshak, 1953.

Christmas card; late 19th century. Colour lithograph.

Page from *A is for Apple Pie* by Kate Greenaway. London 1880.

Soft toy cat. English(?), *c*.1920. BGM.

Cat with a Fish; Anon, Indian (Khaligat), *c*.1890. Watercolour.

Theatre Bilderbuch; Christmas scene from a pop-up book. German *c*.1885. BGM.

Dick Whittington Pantomime Poster; *c*.1897. Colour lithograph.

Page from *A Peep into Catland* by Constance Howell, 1890. Renier Collection, BGM.

(BGM is the Bethnal Green Museum of Childhood, a branch of The Victoria and Albert Museum)

Cover illustration: Christmas card; late 19th century. Colour lithograph.

Back cover illustration: Japanese cat. Colour print. Renier Collection, BGM.